General Knowledge Trivia Quiz Book II

Rick Campbell

BARNES
&NOBLE
BOOKS
NEW YORK

The author wishes to thank all those who provided qustions, expertise and/or encouragement: Sharon Bosley, Mike Ferrari, Mark Lundquist, Heather Russell Revesz, and Sallye Leventhal.

2001 Barnes & Noble Books

ISBN 0-7607-2667-1

Text design by Lundquist Design, New York

Printed and bound in the United States of America

01 02 03 MP 9 8 7 6 5 4 3 2 1

OPM

Q: Why are oil, gas, and coal called fossil fuels?

Q: Where is the largest oil field in the world?

Q: How many gallons are in a barrel of oil?

Q: Where was oil first discovered in the United States?

Q: Where was the first oil well in Texas?

Q: What does OPEC stand for?

A: Because they are composed of the remains of organisms that lived long ago. Over the course of millions of years, these organisms decompose, and are converted into oil, gas, and coal.

A: The largest oil field in the world is the Ghawar field in Saudi Arabia. The largest oil field in the United States is the Permian Basin in western Texas and eastern New Mexico.

A: The barrel, a standard measure of crude oil, contains 42 U.S. gallons.

A: The first oil well in the United States was in Titusville, Pennsylvania, where Colonel Edwin L. Drake drilled the world's first oil well in August 1859.

A: Spindletop, near Beaumont in East Texas, was Texas's first oil gusher, drilled in 1901. It was the beginning of the state's oil boom.

A: The Organization of Petroleum-Exporting Countries.

Q: What animal is a yak?

Q: Where are pandas found?

Q: Are pandas bears?

Q: What is the world's tallest animal?

Q: What is the largest living rodent?

A: A yak is a large, long-haired ox native to the high plateaus and mountains of Tibet, where the climate is cold and dry. The males are more than six feet high at the shoulder and weigh more than one ton. The wild yak, which is larger than the domesticated yak, is considered to be an endangered species.

A: In the wild, pandas are found only in three provinces of China: the Sichuan, Yunnan, and Shaanxi. Though their habitat once covered as much as 300,000 square miles, these migrating animals now live within an 83,000 square mile territory.

A: Researchers are divided—most say they are bears, but some others believe that they are more closely related to raccoons.

A: The male giraffe, which is the tallest of all animals, averages 17 feet in height.

A: The capybara, a semi-aquatic rodent of South America, is about two feet tall at the shoulder, and can weigh more than a hundred pounds. Capybaras are shorthaired, brownish rodents, with blunt snouts, short legs, small ears, and almost no tail. South American capybaras can be up to four feet long; Panamanian capybaras are a little smaller. They are vegetarians, and like to eat in people's gardens.

Q: At the time of the arrival of the Europeans, what was the range of the American bison in North America?

Q: What are the opening words of the Declaration of Independence?

Q: Who wrote the Declaration of Independence?

Q: What is the first sentence of the Constitution of the United States of America?

Q: What are the opening words of Abraham Lincoln's Gettysburg Address?

A: The American bison, commonly known as the buffalo, once roamed over all of North America, coast-to-coast, all the way from the West to the eastern seaboard. The size of the herd was estimated to be as high as 50 million animals. By 1900, there were fewer than 1500 bison left.

A: "When in the Course of human Events, it becomes necessary for one People to dissolve the Political Bands which have connected them with another..."

A: Thomas Jefferson spent eighteen days, from June 11 to June 28, 1776, drafting the Declaration of Independence. Jefferson incorporated changes suggested by Benjamin Franklin and John Adams.

A: "We the People of the United States, in Order to form a more perfect Union, establish Justice, insure domestic Tranquility, provide for the common defence, promote the general Welfare, and secure the Blessings of Liberty to ourselves and our Posterity, do ordain and establish this Constitution for the United States of America."

A: Given November 19, 1863, on the battlefield near Gettysburg, Pennsylvania:
"Four score and seven years ago, our fathers brought forth upon this continent a new nation: conceived in liberty, and dedicated to the proposition that all men are created equal."

Q: Who said the following: "We hold these truths to be self-evident, that all men and women are created equal"?

Q: What is the Nineteenth Amendment to the U.S. Constitution?

Q: What was the Eighteenth Amendment, and when was it passed?

Q: How many voting members are there in the United States House of Representatives? How many Senators are there in the U.S. Congress?

Q: How many senators does each state have in the United States Senate? How many years are there in a Senator's term?

A: This is a quote of Elizabeth Cady Stanton, who made this statement at the Women's Rights Convention in 1848.

A: Adopted on August 26, 1920, the Nineteenth Amendment gives women the right to vote. "The right of citizens of the United States to vote shall not be denied or abridged by the United States or any State on account of sex."

A: The Eighteenth Amendment, which was adopted on January 29, 1919, prohibited the manufacture, sale, importation, and exportation of intoxicating liquors. Prohibition was repealed by the Twenty-First Amendment, which was adopted on December 5, 1933.

A: There are 435 voting members of the U.S. House of Representatives; in addition, there are non-voting delegates from the District of Columbia, Guam, American Samoa, the Virgin Islands, as well as a resident commissioner from Puerto Rico. The U.S. Senate has one hundred Senators.

A: There are two senators from each state; each is elected for a term of six years.

Q: How many members of the U.S. House of Representatives does each state have?

Q: Which seven states have only one representative in the United States House of Representatives?

Q: Name the first thirteen states to be admitted to the United States.

Q: Which eleven states seceded from the Union during the Civil War?

Q: Twenty-three states of the United States are on seacoasts. Can you name them?

A: Population determines the number of representatives per state in the House of Representatives. As of 2001, the numbers of representatives per state ranges from one in states with lower populations, to fifty-two representatives (California).

A: As of 2001, Alaska, Delaware, Montana, North Dakota, South Dakota, Vermont, and Wyoming have only one member of the United States House of Representatives.

A: In the order of their statehood: Delaware, Pennsylvania, New Jersey, Georgia, Connecticut, Massachusetts, Maryland, South Carolina, New Hampshire, Virginia, New York, North Carolina, and Rhode Island.

A: South Carolina, Mississippi, Florida, Alabama, Georgia, Louisiana, Texas, Virginia, Arkansas, North Carolina, and Tennessee formed the Confederate States of America in 1861.

A: Starting in the Northeast and going down the East Coast: Maine, New Hampshire, Massachusetts, Rhode Island, Connecticut, New York, New Jersey, Delaware, Maryland, Virginia, North Carolina, South Carolina, Georgia, and Florida. Continuing with Florida, and crossing the Gulf of Mexico: Alabama, Mississippi, Louisiana, and Texas. On the Pacific: Alaska, Washington, Oregon, California, and Hawaii.

Q: Six states do not have mansions for their governors to live in. Which six states do not supply the state's chief executive with a residence?

Q: The capital city of a state is not always the largest city in the state. What are the capital cities of the following states: Kentucky? Wisconsin? Vermont? Pennsylvania? California? Washington?

Q: Did P. T. Barnum ever serve in an elected office?

Q: Was it P. T. Barnum who said, "there's a sucker born every minute"?

Q: What movie character was famous for saying, "What's up, Doc?"

A: Arizona, California, Idaho, Massachusetts, Rhode Island, and Vermont do not supply mansions for their Governor. They do supply cars for the Governors to get to work.

A: Frankfort, Kentucky; Madison, Wisconsin; Montpelier, Vermont; Harrisburg, Pennsylvania; Sacramento, California; and Olympia, Washington.

A: Phineas Taylor Barnum was elected to the Connecticut state legislature in 1865. He had also served as the mayor of Bridgeport, Connecticut.

A: Although he was known for being a shameless huckster, there is no proof that he actually made that remark. In addition to his famous circus, Barnum was the showman who first presented to America the Cardiff Giant, Tom Thumb, and the original Siamese twins, Chang and Eng. He began his career hawking an elderly, blind African-American woman as being the 161-year-old former nurse of George Washington.

A: Bugs Bunny. Frederick Bean "Tex" Avery (1908–1980) was Bugs's creator, and Mel Blanc (1908–1989) was the voice.

Q: When did Porky Pig make his first movie?

Q: What are the names of the seven diminutive people in Walt Disney's *Snow White and the Seven Dwarfs*?

Q: Where did Walt Disney's seven dwarfs work?

Q: What is the name of the well-known singing group that signed with Motown Records in 1969, and hails from Gary, Indiana? What are the first names of the members of this group?

Q: Which performer has been proclaimed the "King of Pop"? What rock and roller was known as the "King"?

Q: Who is the "Queen of Soul"?

Q: Who is the "Godfather of Soul"?

A: On March 2, 1935, Porky Pig appeared in his first film, *I Haven't Got a Hat*, directed by Friz Freleng. Porky's career developed alongside the career of Warner Brothers's head of animation Chuck Jones. Porky's best-known line is "Th-th-th-that's all, folks!"

A: In Walt Disney's 1937 adaptation of the old fairy tale, the forest-dwelling dwarfs have the names of Dopey, Sneezy, Grumpy, Happy, Bashful, Doc, and Sleepy.

A: They worked in the mines, digging for diamonds. They sang "Heigh-ho" on their way to and from the mines. They also liked to whistle while they worked.

A: The Jackson Five. Jackie (born Sigmund), Tito (born Toriano), Jermaine, Marlon, and Michael.

A: Michael Jackson (without his brothers) was dubbed the "King of Pop." Elvis Presley, who happens to be Michael's former father-in-law, was known as the "King."

A: Aretha Franklin.

A: James Brown.

Q: What singer was called the "Chairman of the Board"?

Q: What was the biggest hit by the soul group named The Chairmen of the Board?

Q: Which father and daughter combination had a Top 40 hit singing a duet?

Q: What was Elvis Presley's middle name? Where was he born? Where and when did he die?

Q: Is Elvis's middle name misspelled on his tombstone?

A: Frank Sinatra, also known as "Old Blue Eyes."

A: Although The Chairmen of the Board had a few minor hits, their biggest chartbuster was their debut single, "Give Me Just A Little More Time," released in 1970 on Invicta Records.

A: Only one father and daughter combination qualifies as producing a solid Top 40 hit singing a duet: Frank Sinatra and Nancy Sinatra had a big hit in 1967, "Something Stupid." There are two other recordings that could be considered, however. In 1960, Carla Thomas and her father Rufus Thomas recorded a song that was a hit in the Memphis area, "Cause I Love You." And in 1991, Natalie Cole sang a tribute "duet" with her late father, Nat "King" Cole, by recording her voice track with his original recording of "Unforgettable."

A: Elvis Aron Presley was born in Tupelo, Mississippi on January 8, 1935. Although there are those who believe otherwise, the general opinion is that he died at the age of 42 at his home, Graceland, in Memphis, on August 16, 1977.

A: Yes. Elvis's full name is Elvis Aron Presley, but on his grave his middle name is spelled incorrectly as "Aaron," with two a's. People who believe Elvis is not dead point to this fact as part of the evidence of a conspiracy.

Q: How many movies were Elvis Presley and Nancy Sinatra in together?

Q: What was Elvis's occupation before he became famous as a rock and roll singer?

Q: Who was Colonel Tom Parker?

Q: When and where was Louis Armstrong born? When and where did Louis Armstrong die?

Q: Louis Armstrong appeared in many films over the years. What was the last film he made?

Q: The following musicians are best known by their nicknames. What were their birth names? Dizzy Gillespie? Duke Ellington? Count Basie? Cannonball Adderley? Fats Waller?

A: Just one—the easy-to-forget *Speedway* (1968)—directed by Norman Taurog. Elvis plays Steve Grayson, a stock car racer who owes the Internal Revenue Service hundreds of thousands of dollars, due to bad accounting practices by his accountant, played by Bill Bixby. Nancy Sinatra plays an IRS agent who is supposed to collect the money.

A: Elvis was a truck driver in Memphis.

A: Colonel Tom Parker was Elvis Presley's manager. Parker had been a carnival pitchman before turning to the management of performers. He had worked with country stars Eddy Arnold and Hank Snow before becoming Elvis's manager.

A: Although he always claimed to be have been born on the Fourth of July, 1900, recently uncovered records indicate that Louis Armstrong was born on August 4, 1901 in New Orleans. He died in his sleep of a heart attack in New York City on July 6, 1971.

A: The last film that Louis Armstrong made before his death was 1969's *Hello, Dolly!* directed by Gene Kelly, and starring Barbra Streisand. Louis, of course, sang the title song.

A: John Gillespie, Edward Kennedy Ellington, William Basie, Julian Adderley, and Thomas Waller.

Q: Which bird is the fastest flyer?

Q: What is the largest living bird?

Q: What is the world's smallest living bird?

Q: Where do secretary birds live? How do secretary birds subdue their prey?

Q: Do birds have the sense of smell?

Q: Do any mammals lay eggs?

A: The peregrine falcon can reach speeds of up to 200 miles per hour when diving for such prey as doves and pigeons.

A: The largest extant bird is the ostrich. Male ostriches grow to about eight feet tall and weigh 300 pounds. Ostriches may be flightless birds, but they are fast on their feet, capable of running 45 miles per hour.

A: The bee hummingbird, native to Cuba, weighs less than one ounce and measures about two inches.

A: Secretary birds, three-foot-tall birds with long legs, live in Africa south of the Sahara. These birds of prey use their strong legs to kickbox, pounding the daylights out of reptiles, snakes, lizards, and small ground rodents. They are named secretary birds because the plume feathers at the back of their heads resemble old-fashioned quill pens.

A: Based on scientific studies of bird brains, the sense of smell seems to be underdeveloped in most birds. Not too surprisingly, a large part of the brain is connected to sight and balance—both very important when flying.

A: Yes, both the spiny anteater and the duck-billed platypus are mammals and lay eggs.

Q: What kind of animal is a pinniped?

Q: What is the largest pinniped?

Q: What is a polar bear's favorite treat?

Q: What fish is the world's largest?

Q: What is the world's smallest fish?

A: A pinniped is an aquatic carnivorous mammal that has four flippers. The name "pinniped" refers to the animal being "fin-footed." Seals, sea lions, and walruses are all pinnipeds.

A: The largest pinniped is the elephant seal, which can weigh as much as four tons.

A: Polar bears, the world's largest land predators, like to eat seals.

A: The world's largest fish is the whale shark, which can grow to longer than 40 feet and can weigh as much as 30,000 pounds. Despite their huge size, they are not considered a threat to people. The whale shark is what's known as a filter feeder—it swims with its six-foot-wide mouth open, exposing its 600 tiny teeth, gathering small fish, crustaceans, and squid. The largest known whale shark was captured in 1919. It was over 60 feet long, and weighed 80,000 pounds! That's a lot of filter feeding!

A: The smallest fish is the goby, which grows only as long as 1 centimeter (less than half an inch); it swims in coral reefs in the western Pacific.

Q: Some fish have cartilage for support, others have skeletons. What fish is the largest bony fish?

Q: What fish is the fastest swimmer?

Q: What is the largest living animal on land or in the sea?

Q: What is the largest land animal?

Q: What are Gila monsters? Are they native to the United States?

A: The world's largest bony fish is the ocean sunfish, also known as the mola mola, which can grow to ten feet in length and weigh as much as 3000 pounds. There are larger fish, including sharks, but they have cartilage for support, rather than bones.

A: The sailfish is considered the fastest of all fish species. It is difficult to measure the speeds of fish, but the sailfish has been clocked at speeds of over sixty miles per hour.

A: The blue whale, which is eighty to ninety feet long, and has an average weight of 280,000 pounds! Its tongue alone weighs one ton! Not only is it the largest animal on earth, it is the loudest. Blue whales emit loud, low frequency rumbling sounds that register louder than a jet engine or a heavy metal rock band.

A: The African elephant. The world's largest land animal can weigh more than eight tons and measure twelve to thirteen feet tall. The Indian elephant is a smaller elephant, but still can weigh as much as six tons.

A: The Gila monster is a large, venomous lizard native to the deserts of Arizona and the American Southwest. It has a yellow and black tail, is eighteen inches long, with a stout body and a large head. Although it generally moves around slowly, it can bite suddenly and then hold on tenaciously to its victims.

Q: How large were mammoths?

Q: What prominent feature do the group of mammals known as proboscideans have in common?

Q: Dolphins call to each other, but do dolphins have vocal cords?

Q: Did the United States Navy use trained dolphins in Vietnam?

A: The prehistoric proboscideans known as mammoths were ten to fourteen feet tall, and could weigh up to 20,000 pounds. The mammoth had a shaggy coat, a long trunk, slender tusks, and lived in grasslands. Frozen, preserved mammoths have been found, organs intact, in the Siberian permafrost.

A: A proboscidean is a mammal with a long trunk-like snout. There are only two extant proboscideans—the African (*Loxodonta africana*) and Asian (*Elephas maximus*) elephants. Elephants are also called *pachyderms*, a term that refers to their thick skin.

A: Dolphins, who are aquatic mammals, do not have vocal cords, nor do they speak with their mouths. They are able to make noises using their breath through the blowholes on the tops of their bodies.

A: Yes, dolphins were trained to conduct surveillance patrols with a camera held in their mouths, and work with frogmen to deliver equipment and to locate underwater mines and obstacles. The United States Navy also used trained dolphins in the 1987 Persian Gulf War. The Navy denies rumors that the dolphins have been used as suicide bombers to attack enemy ships and swimmers.

Q: What is unusual about pregnant seahorses?

Q: What is a marsupial?

Q: What was the date of the launch of the world's first artificial satellite?

Q: When did the United States launch its first satellite?

Q: What was the name of the first human sent into space?

Q: What was the name of the first American sent into space?

A: Pregnant seahorses are male. The female seahorse transfers her eggs into the male's exterior abdominal pouch. The male grows visibly "pregnant" within a few weeks. Embryos hatch in his pouch and are incubated there.

A: A marsupial is a mammal with a pouch on the abdomen of the female, such as kangaroos, bandicoots, wombats, koalas, and opossums.

A: The Soviet Union launched the communications satellite *Sputnik* into orbit on October 4, 1957. The United States countered by putting out several pop songs with "sputnik" in the lyrics.

A: The first United States satellite was the *Explorer I*, launched on Jan. 31, 1958, almost four months after *Sputnik*.

A: Soviet cosmonaut Yuri Gagarin became the first human in space on April 12, 1961. His *Vostok I* spacecraft orbited the earth once.

A: On May 5, 1961, astronaut Alan B. Shepard, Jr. became the first American in space in a 15 minute, 28 second sub-orbital flight. John H. Glenn, Jr. became the first U.S. astronaut to orbit the Earth in 1962.

Q: Who was the first woman in space?

Q: Who was the first man on the moon?

Q: What were the astronaut's first words when he first stood on the moon's surface?

Q: Where is the lunar buggy now?

Q: Does the planet Mars have moons?

A: Velentina Tereshkova became the first woman to travel in space. She made 45 revolutions of the earth in the spacecraft *Vostok 6* on June 16–19, 1963. The first American woman in space was Sally Ride, who made her first trip aboard the shuttle *Challenger* on June 18–24, 1983.

A: At 10:56 PM EDT, July 20, 1969, American astronaut Neil Armstrong became the first person to set foot on the Moon. Armstrong and Edwin "Buzz" Aldrin left the *Eagle* lunar landing module for more than two hours during which time they played a little golf, and rode around in the lunar buggy. Meanwhile, astronaut Michael Collins orbited the moon in the Command module.

A: "That's one small step for [a] man, one giant leap for Mankind."

A: Still on the moon. Luckily, the moon has free parking.

A: Yes. Mars has two small moons: Phobos and Deimos. They were discovered in 1877 by Asaph Hall, and named after the horses in Roman mythology who pulled Mar's chariot.

Q: What is the largest island in the world?

Q: What is the largest continent in the world?

Q: Where is the Gobi desert?

Q: What percentage of the world's land surface is desert?

Q: Who were the world's first surfers?

Q: What name was Hawaii given when the Europeans discovered it?

A: The island of Greenland, in the North Atlantic Ocean, is the world's largest island, covering 840,000 square miles. Greenland is a dependency of Denmark. The island of Australia is larger than Greenland, but it is considered a continent.

A: Asia, which is 17,300,000 square miles.

A: The Gobi desert is a desert and semidesert region of Central Asia stretching across the Mongolian People's Republic and the Inner Mongolia region of China. Its total area is about 500,000 square miles.

A: Twenty percent.

A: Captain James Cook was the first European to visit the Hawaiian Islands in 1778. When he arrived, riding the ocean waves on a narrow surfboard was already a popular sport in Hawaii.

A: In 1778, English Captain Cook named the islands we now call Hawaii the Sandwich Islands, for the Earl of Sandwich.

Q: Where did the sandwich get its name?

Q: What is the latitude of the equator?

Q: What is the longitude of the prime meridian?

Q: What is the International Date Line?

A: John Montagu, the Fourth Earl of Sandwich (1718–1792), was a British nobleman who served as the Secretary of State and First Lord of the Admiralty, and is credited with popularizing the idea of sandwiches. He loved to gamble, and hated to leave the gaming table. Having meat served between two slices of bread allowed the Earl to eat while he stayed in the game. Soon, this way of serving food was named after him.

A: 0°. The equator is a great circle around the earth that has a latitude of zero degrees. It is the base line from which latitude is calculated over the globe. The equator is equidistant from the two geographical poles, dividing the earth into the northern and southern hemispheres.

A: 0°. The prime meridian has a longitude of zero degrees and runs through Greenwich, England. It separates the east and west longitudes.

A: The International Date Line, halfway round the earth from Greenwich, roughly following the 180° meridian, is the line where each calendar day begins. The date on the western side of the line (in the Eastern Hemisphere) is one day later than the date on the eastern side of the line (in the Western Hemisphere).

Q: When a new London Bridge was built in 1973, the bridge built in 1831 was taken down. Where is it now?

Q: Where is the Ponte Vecchio?

Q: Why is the bridge in Venice called the "Bridge of Sighs"?

Q: What was the Tay Railway Bridge Disaster?

A: The London Bridge that was built in 1831 is now in Lake Havasu City, Arizona. It used to cross the Thames River in London, England. The 1831 bridge, designed by John Rennie, was itself a replacement for the medieval London Bridge of nursery rhyme fame.

A: Considered to be an outstanding engineering achievement of the Italian Middle Ages, the Ponte Vecchio is a much-photographed bridge that crosses over the Arno River at Florence.

A: The "Bridge of Sighs" received its nickname in the seventeenth century, inspired by the sighs of prisoners as they were led over the bridge on their way to the prison cells. This bridge over the Rio di Palazzo, built in 1600, connected the prisons to the inquisitor's rooms in the main palace.

A: Just under two miles in length, the railway bridge over the Tay estuary in Scotland was the longest bridge in the world when it was opened in 1878. On December 28,1879, part of the center section of the bridge collapsed during a storm with severe winds, just as the evening train carrying 75 passengers from Edinburgh to Dundee passed onto the bridge. The disaster shocked the general public, and sent shock waves through the Victorian engineering profession.

Q: In 1940, what was the nickname for the Tacoma Narrows Bridge across Puget Sound?

Q: Where was the first skyscraper built?

Q: What is the tallest building in the world?

Q: What is the tallest building in the United States?

Q: What building is the largest office building in the world, in terms of ground space?

A: The Tacoma Narrows Bridge was nicknamed "Galloping Gertie" because, on November 7, 1940, just four months after the bridge's opening, the deck twisted, rolled, and buckled under a wind of 42 miles per hour. Needless to say, the bridge had engineering and design problems. The Tacoma Narrows Bridge was replaced in 1950 by a new span.

A: The building considered to be the world's first skyscraper is William Le Baron Jenney's ten-story Home Insurance Company Building in Chicago. Built in 1883, it was the first fully steel-framed building, using steel-girder construction, and supported by internal construction, rather than by load-bearing walls.

A: The Petronas Towers in Kuala Lumpur are the tallest buildings in the world. They are twin towers, each 1,483 feet tall and 88 stories.

A: The Sears Tower in Chicago, which is 110 stories and 1,450 feet tall, and is the second-tallest building in the world. It was completed in 1974.

A: The Pentagon, which was built in sixteen months in 1941–1943, covers an area of 34 acres, and has a gross floor area of 6.6 million square feet, as well as 7,748 windows.

Q: What is the tallest structure in the world?

Q: What is a rip tide?

Q: Who was Patrick Henry? What is his famous quote?

Q: Who were Mason and Dixon? What is the Mason-Dixon Line?

A: The CNN Tower in Toronto, built as a television transmission tower, is 1,815 feet tall.

A: Rip tides are formed when water that is pushed up on shore cannot easily return, and becomes trapped inside the break near shore. As gravity pulls the water back toward the sea, a river-like current develops, eroding a channel, and creating what is known as a rip current, or rip tide. It is estimated that 80% of the rescues by lifeguards at America's surf beaches are due to people being caught in rip currents.

A: Patrick Henry was a famous orator, an influential statesman, and governor of Virginia at the time of the American Revolution. He is best known for saying "Give me liberty or give me death!" at a convention in 1775. He was referring to taking up the cause of arming the militia.

A: In 1763, Charles Mason and Jeremiah Dixon were commissioned by the heirs of William Penn and Lord Baltimore to settle an old boundary dispute between Pennsylvania and Maryland. Proceeding along the parallel of latitude 39°43′17.6″ N, their work was limited to the two states of Pennsylvania and Maryland. Later, the Mason and Dixon Line became known as the boundary between free states and slave states, and is now regarded as the boundary between the North and the South.

Q: When was gold first discovered in the Yukon?

Q: What was the path of the Oregon Trail? What was its significance?

Q: How long did it take Robert Fulton's steamship to make the trip from New York City to Albany, New York?

Q: How many immigrants passed through Ellis Island?

A: On August 17, 1896, three men (Skookum Jim, Tagish Charlie, and American George Carmack) discovered gold in Rabbit Creek, which they renamed Bonanza Creek. The 1898 Klondike Gold Rush was on. Over 100,000 adventurers arrived over the next few years.

A: The Oregon Trail ran about 2,000 miles, from Independence, Missouri, to the Columbia River region in Oregon. The Trail generally follows the Platte River to its headwaters, then crosses the mountains, and then follows the Snake River to the Columbia River. It was a trail first used by fur traders and missionaries, but, beginning in 1842, wagon trains kicked off a massive move west on the Oregon Trail. More than 500,000 people traveled west on the Trail over the next twenty-five years, until the transcontinental railroad was completed in 1869.

A: Beginning on August 17, 1807, Robert Fulton made the first practical steamboat trip, a 150 mile voyage from New York City to Albany, in 32 hours.

A: Twenty-two million people passed through Ellis Island, which is situated in New York Harbor, in its years of operation as the United States's principal immigration reception center from 1892 to 1924.

Q: How did the bazooka gun get its name?

Q: What was the name of Bob Burns's radio show?

Q: Why is thoroughbred horse racing called "the sport of kings"?

Q: What is the Triple Crown in thoroughbred horse racing?

Q: How does a batter win the Triple Crown in baseball? Who was the last person to win it?

A: As unusual as it sounds, the armor-piercing hollow-tube weapon developed during the war was named after the humorous musical instrument that radio entertainer Bob Burns had fashioned from two gas pipes and a funnel.

A: Bob Burns had a radio show that was popular in the '30s and '40s, called "The Arkansas Traveler." His show has been described as a precursor to *Hee-Haw.*

A: Because European royalty was interested in thoroughbred racing. As early as 1110, England's King Henry I had imported an Arabian stallion from Spain, and horse racing became a favorite pastime of the English royalty and nobility. In the mid-1600s, King Charles II of England was a racing enthusiast and did much to revive the popularity of the sport.

A: The three major U.S. races for horses three years of age—the Kentucky Derby, the Preakness Stakes, and the Belmont Stakes—comprise the Triple Crown. The last Triple Crown winner was Affirmed, who out-dueled Alydar in all three races in 1978.

A: In baseball, the batter who leads the league in batting average, home runs, and RBIs is the winner of the Triple Crown. The last winner of the Triple Crown in baseball was Carl Yastrzemski of the Boston Red Sox in 1967.

Q: When did the Yankees first wear pinstripes?

Q: In what cities did the baseball Braves make their home before they moved to Atlanta?

Q: What famous player, one of the best of all time, finished his baseball career playing with the Braves in 1935?

Q: When was the spitball made illegal in major league baseball?

Q: When was the first World Series played?

A: On April 11, 1912, pinstripes first appeared on the uniforms of the Highlanders, who were the forerunners of the New York Yankees.

A: Boston and Milwaukee. Before they were the Atlanta Braves, they were the Boston Red Stockings (1876–1883), the Boston Beaneaters (1883–1907), the Boston Doves (1908–1912), and the Boston Braves (1913–1952) before they moved to Milwaukee, where they played from 1953 to 1965. In 1966, the Braves became the Atlanta Braves.

A: George Herman "Babe" Ruth played in 28 games for the Boston Braves in 1935. The "Sultan of Swat" announced his retirement on June 2, 1935.

A: In 1920, major league baseball banned the spitball, but allowed all the pitchers currently throwing it at the time to continue to do so. When pitcher Burleigh Grimes retired in 1934 (with 270 wins), the legal spitball was dead.

A: Although there had been other post-season championships played as early as 1884, the first World Series Championship was played in 1903. The Pittsburgh Pirates and the Boston Pilgrims (later the Red Sox) met in a best-of-nine-game post-season series in September 1903. Boston upset the favored Pirates, five games to three.

Q: What was the "Black Sox scandal" of 1919?

Q: When was the first telecast of a major league baseball game?

Q: Who played for the Brooklyn Dodgers for 16 years (1940–1956), but never got a hit?

Q: What countries does the Nile pass through on its way to the Mediterranean Sea?

Q: The Mississippi River forms one of the borderlines of ten different states on its voyage from its source in Minnesota down to the Gulf of Mexico. Can you name the states?

A: In the most famous scandal in baseball history, eight players from the Chicago White Sox (later scorned as the Black Sox) were accused of throwing the World Series against the Cincinnati Reds. The players involved were banned from professional baseball for life.

A: In the first major league baseball telecast on August 26, 1939, the Brooklyn Dodgers split a doubleheader with the Cincinnati Reds at Ebbets Field, Brooklyn, broadcast on W2XBS, the RCA station in New York.

A: Gladys Gooding, the stadium organist. She was the first of the stadium organists. Ms. Gooding also played at Madison Square Garden for the basketball and hockey games of the New York Knicks and the New York Rangers. She didn't score any baskets or goals, either.

A: The basin of the world's longest river includes Burundi, Rwanda, Tanzania, Kenya, Uganda, Congo, Sudan, Ethiopia, and Egypt.

A: After splitting the twin cities of Minneapolis and St. Paul, the Mississippi forms parts of the borderline of the states of Minnesota, Wisconsin, Iowa, Illinois, Missouri, Kentucky, Tennessee, Arkansas, Mississippi, and Louisiana. It empties into the Gulf of Mexico.

Q: Where do you find the bones that have the nicknames hammer, anvil, and stirrup? What important role do they play in the human body?

Q: What is the smallest bone in the body?

Q: In what year was Microsoft founded?

Q: When was Apple Computer founded?

Q: When was U.S. Steel founded?

Q: What did Meyer Lansky have to say about the size of the organized crime industry in the United States?

Q: What letters are the most valuable in *Scrabble®*?

A: These bones, formally known as the malleus, incus, and stapes, are three small bones located in the ear canal and called ossicles. They are essential to the hearing process; they vibrate in a chain reaction and conduct sound waves through the middle ear.

A: The stapes, a.k.a. the stirrup.

A: In 1975, Bill Gates and Paul Allen began developing software by developing a *BASIC* computer language.

A: On April 1, 1976, Steven Wozniak and Steven Jobs, who had been friends in high school, founded the Apple Computer Company. Both had been working in Silicon Valley, California when Wozniak designed what would become the first Apple computer.

A: The United States Steel Corporation was formed in 1901. At that time, it was the largest business enterprise ever launched. U.S. Steel was the first billion-dollar enterprise in American history.

A: "We're bigger than U.S. Steel."

A: The letters "Q" and "Z" are each worth 10 points. "J" and "X" are worth 8 each.

Q: Did the film *Casablanca* win an Oscar®?

Q: What was Rick's last name in *Casablanca*?

Q: What was the Burma Road?

Q: How many miles of public roads are there in the U.S.?

Q: What is the origin of the word "maverick"?

A: Yes, it won three Academy Awards in 1943, including Best Picture. It also won Oscars® for Best Director for Michael Curtiz, and Best Screenplay for Julius and Philip Epstein and Howard Koch.

A: Rick Blaine was the character played by Humphrey Bogart. Ingrid Bergman played Ilsa Lund Laszlo.

A: The Burma Road was a 700 mile long road built during World War Two, leading from Lashio, Burma to Kunming, China. It was used by the Allies for transporting supplies to China for use against Japan.

A: There are estimated to be over four million miles of public roads in the United States, enough to circle the globe 150 times.

A: Samuel A. Maverick (1803–1870) was a Texas pioneer who did not brand his calves. Maverick's herd was allowed to wander and gave rise to the term *maverick*, which denotes a stray, unbranded calf. Today, the word also refers to a person who refuses to go along with the crowd.

Q: Who invented the *guillotine*?

Q: Match the capital cities and the countries.

Canada	**Budapest**
Hungary	**Wellington**
New Zealand	**Nicosia**
Tanzania	**Ottawa**
Cyprus	**Dar-Es-Salaam**
Pakistan	**Islamabad**

Q: Who were the Celts?

Q: Which peoples speak Celtic languages?

A: The guillotine was invented by French doctor Joseph Guillotin (1738–1814), who argued for a quick, painless method of capital punishment. Doctor Guillotin worked together with German engineer Tobias Schmidt to build a prototype guillotine machine, with the blade at an oblique 45-degree angle. The first guillotining took place on April 25, 1792. Thousands of people were guillotined during the French Revolution.

A: Canada—Ottawa; Hungary—Budapest; New Zealand—Wellington; Tanzania—Dar-Es-salaam; Cyprus—Nicosia; Pakistan—Islamabad.

A: Also spelled *Kelt*, the Celts were an early Indo-European people who migrated over much of Europe from the 2nd millennium B.C.E. to the 1st century B.C.E. They ranged from the British Isles and northern Spain to as far east as the Black Sea.

A: Although the majority of residents speak English or French, the native languages of Ireland, Scotland, Wales, the Isle of Man, and Brittany are all Celtic languages.

Q: Who were the Druids?

Q: What is a Gordian knot?

Q: When did Alexander the Great live?

Q: What was the name of Alexander's horse?

A: No one knows exactly, but it is believed that the Druids were the priests of the ancient Celtic people. They filled the roles of priests, scholars, teachers, and judges in Celtic society. It is believed that the stone circles found in Britain, the most well known being Stonehenge, are associated with the Druids. The earliest known records of the Druids come from the third century B.C.E.

A: In Greek mythology, Gordius, king of Phrygia, tied a knot so intricate that no one could undo it. An oracle said that the one to undo it will be the future ruler of Asia. When Alexander the Great was unable to untie the Gordian knot, he cut it through with one stroke of his sword, thereby solving a perplexing problem by a simple, decisive action. He had cut the Gordian knot.

A: Alexander the Great was born in 356 B.C.E. He was the King of Macedonia who conquered much of the ancient world from Asia Minor to Egypt and India. Alexander is considered a military genius. He died in 323 B.C.E.

A: Buchephalas, a black stallion with a white mark on his forehead. When Buchephalas died, Alexander the Great had a state funeral for him.

Q: Where was the Battle of Bunker Hill fought? When?

Q: What was "the Boston Massacre"?

Q: Did German U-boats land in the United States during the Second World War?

Q: Where is the world's longest underground cave system?

A: The Battle of Bunker Hill was actually fought on Breed's Hill, Massachusetts, on June 17, 1775. The British troops under the command of General Howe, were ordered to charge the position held by the American Patriots on Breed's Hill. On their third attempt to take the hill, the Americans were forced to retreat. Although it was a British victory, the battle showed the patriots that the British were not invincible, encouraging the Patriot cause.

A: In March 1770, in an early skirmish of what would become the American Revolution, British troops fired on American colonists who were throwing snowballs. Five colonists were killed.

A: Yes, the Germans landed U-boats on New York's Long Island, and in Florida. Four German agents were put ashore at each location with instructions to destroy American factories. The agents from the Long Island landing were spotted right away, and the FBI was soon hot on the trail. One of the German agents turned himself in, and the FBI was able to round up the rest of the agents.

A: The cave system in Kentucky's Mammoth Cave National Park is the world's longest cave system. Mammoth Cave connects to the Flint Ridge cave system—the mapped underground passages have a combined length of more than 345 miles.

Q: Is it stalactites or stalagmites that hang from the ceiling of caves?

Q: Who was Floyd Collins?

Q: What is the Chinook wind?

Q: What is the strongest recorded earthquake in history?

A: Icicle-shaped stalactites, which are formed by ground water dripping, hang from the ceiling. One handy tip is that the letter "c" in stal<u>ac</u>tite stands for the ceiling, and the "g" in stal<u>ag</u>mite is for the structure that sticks up from the ground. Sometimes, the two calcites meet and form solid pillars.

A: In 1925, Floyd Collins, then considered to be one of the world's top spelunkers, was trapped by a falling rock in Kentucky's Sand Cave. He was wedged in, 150 feet below the surface, and ended up dying after being trapped for fifteen days. The new medium of radio brought the unfolding story of the attempted rescue to the living rooms of the entire country.

A: The Chinooks are the warm dry winds that flow down from the eastern slopes of the Rocky Mountains and have been known to raise temperatures by 30 degrees Fahrenheit in only a few hours.

A: The strongest recorded earthquake was in Chile in 1960—the magnitude was 9.5 on the Richter scale. The main shock set up a series of seismic sea waves that caused extensive damage as far away as Hawaii and Japan. The next strongest earthquake was at Prince William Sound in Alaska in 1964—9.2. It is also the most severe earthquake in United States history.

Q: What was the largest earthquake in the history of the 48 contiguous United States?

Q: Where is the world's largest active volcano?

Q: What is the southernmost land on Earth?

Q: What is the northernmost land on Earth?

Q: Who was the first woman to be elected governor of a state?

Q: Which state was the first to give women the right to vote?

A: On February 7, 1812, there was an earthquake with a magnitude of at least 7.9 in New Madrid, Missouri.

A: The most massive volcano in the world is Mauna Loa in Hawaii, at 13,677 feet. Its dome is 75 miles long and 64 miles wide, and its lava flows occupy more than 2,000 square miles. Mauna Loa averages one eruption every 3.5 years.

A: The land of Antarctica, at the South Pole, is the southernmost land on Earth.

A: Unlike the South Pole, the North Pole is on an ice pack, not on land. The northernmost land is Cape Morris Jessup, Greenland, with a latitude of approximately 84° North.

A: Nellie Tayloe Ross of Wyoming was the nation's first woman governor. She won a special election in 1924 to complete her deceased husband's term.

A: In 1869, Wyoming, which was still a territory, gave women the right to vote. Wyoming became a state in 1890, becoming the first state to grant full voting rights to women. The state motto is "Equal Rights."

Q: Who was "Ma" Ferguson?

Q: Who was the first woman to run for the U.S. presidency?

Q: Who became the first woman to head the government of an Islamic nation?

Q: Who was the first woman to serve as Britain's Prime Minister?

Q: Which animal is the oldest domestic animal?

Q: When were cats first domesticated?

A: The first woman Governor of Texas and second woman in the United States to be elected Governor was Miriam Amanda Wallace Ferguson, wife of former Governor James E. Ferguson, who had been thrown out of office. When James Ferguson failed to get his name on the ballot in 1924, Miriam entered the race. Although "Ma" Ferguson was elected on the same day as Wyoming's Nellie Ross, she was inaugurated fifteen days later. Her nickname came from her initials.

A: In 1872, the Equal Rights Party nominated Victoria Claflin Woodhull for the presidency. This was at a time when, nationwide, women were not allowed to vote.

A: On December 2, 1988, Benazir Bhutto was sworn in as Prime Minister of Pakistan, becoming the first female Prime Minister of an Islamic State.

A: Margaret Thatcher, who assumed the position of Prime Minister in May 1979, had been the Conservative Party Leader of the Opposition since 1970. She resigned her office in November 1990.

A: The dog, which has been domesticated for 12,000 to 14,000 years.

A: Cats were domesticated in ancient Egypt as long as 4,000 years ago.

Q: How many American homes have reptiles as pets?

Q: What breed of dog is the most popular in the United States?

Q: When was the modern game of tennis introduced to England?

Q: What 12th century French game is considered the precursor to lawn tennis?

A: As of 2000, nearly 4 million American households had a reptile as a pet. Turtles, snakes, and frogs are the most popular reptilian pets. More than 63 million households own one or more pets of any kind; dogs and cats remain the most popular.

A: According to the American Kennel Club, Labrador retrievers are the number one registered dog in the U.S., with 172,841 labs registered. The next most popular breeds are golden retrievers (66,300) and German Shepherds (57,660).

A: The standard belief is that Major W. C. Wingfield introduced lawn tennis at a garden party in 1873. He published the first book of rules for what he called "Sphairistiké, or Lawn Tennis" that year and took out a patent on his game in 1874. However, researchers have concluded that there were earlier versions of tennis, and that the first tennis club was established by the Englishman Harry Gem in Leamington in 1872.

A: *Jeu de paume* ("game of the palm"), which was played without rackets.

Q: When was the modern game of tennis introduced to the United States?

Q: When was the first tennis championship tournament held at Wimbledon?

Q: How many Wimbledon singles tournaments did Martina Navratilova win?

Q: Who was the youngest ever Wimbledon champion?

A: Credit is given to Mary Outerbridge of New York for bringing a set of rackets and balls to her brother, a director of the Staten Island Cricket and Baseball Club in 1874. She had seen a tennis match in Bermuda. But, research has shown that William Appleton of Nahant, Massachusetts, may have owned the first lawn tennis set in the United States.

A: In 1877, the Wimbledon club decided to hold a tennis championship, and standardized the rules. They decided on a rectangular court 78 feet long by 27 feet wide, and adopted a method of scoring; these decisions remain part of the modern rules. The first winner of the All-England Championship was Spencer Gore.

A: Martina Navratilova won nine Wimbledon singles tournaments. Her first Wimbledon win was in 1978; she also won in 1979, 1982–1987, and again in 1990. Navratilova, the top ranked woman player from 1982–1986, also won four U.S. Open titles, three Australian Open titles, and two French Open titles.

A: Switzerland's Martina Hingis, who was 15 years, 282 days old when she won in 1996.

Q: Who was the first African-American to win the Wimbledon tournament?

Q: Who was the first African-American male to win a major U.S. tennis title?

Q: Who was Deacon Brodie? What part did he play in literature?

Q: Who was the author of the 1963 novel, *The Spy Who Came in From the Cold*?

A: In 1957, Althea Gibson became the first African-American woman to win at Wimbledon and Forest Hills. That same year, she was named Woman Athlete of the Year by the Associated Press. Gibson was the first African-American to play in the U.S. grass court championships at Forest Hills, N.Y. (1950), and at Wimbledon, England (1951).

A: Arthur Ashe won 51 titles, including the 1968 U.S. Open, the 1970 Australian Open, and the 1975 Wimbledon title. After suffering from a heart attack and undergoing quadruple bypass surgery, Ashe retired as a player in 1980 with a professional record of 818 wins, 260 losses.

A: Deacon Brodie was the inspiration for Robert Louis Stevenson's Dr. Jekyll and Mr. Hyde. Brodie was a pillar of Edinburgh society who lived a double life: straight-laced establishment member turned arch criminal, terrifying Edinburgh in the late 18th century. Nearly a century later, Stevenson told the story of the infamous Mr. Hyde.

A: John le Carré is the nom de plume of David Cornwell, who was born in 1931 in Dorset, England. Le Carré's third novel, *The Spy Who Came in from the Cold*, was the one that secured him a worldwide reputation.

Q: What is George Eliot's real name?

Q: When did Aldous Huxley publish his novel *Brave New World*? When was *1984*, by George Orwell, published?

Q: Who created the library in Alexandria in the fourth century B.C.E.?

Q: What is a theremin?

Q: Where does the word "boycott" come from?

Q: Who first discovered the moons of Jupiter?

A: Mary Ann Evans (1819–1880) who is the author of many literary classics, including *Adam Bede*, *Mill on the Floss*, *Middlemarch*, and *Silas Marner*.

A: Huxley's view of the future was published in 1933; Orwell's story of a future society run by Big Brother and the Thought Police—*1984*—was published in 1949.

A: Ptolemy I, King of Egypt

A: It is an electronic musical instrument invented by Professor Leon Theremin. The theremin is probably best known for its spooky sounds in many old science fiction movies and in the Beach Boys' song "Good Vibrations." A musician plays the theremin by waving his hands around two electrodes, controlling the tone and loudness.

A: The word "boycott" comes from Captain Charles Cunningham Boycott, who was the agent for the Earl of Erne's estates in County Mayo, Ireland. In 1880, when Boycott refused to reduce rents, the tenants shunned Boycott, and avoided any communication with him.

A: Galileo Galilei made the telescope famous for his astronomical observations in 1609. He was the first to provide drawings of the moons of Jupiter and document the phases of Venus.

Q: How long did Britain's Queen Victoria reign?

Q: Who is the author of the following quotes?
"A penny saved is a penny earned."
"Any fool can criticize, condemn and complain, and most fools do."
"Early to bed, early to rise makes a man healthy, wealthy, and wise."
"Fish and visitors smell in three days."
"Never leave that till tomorrow which you can do today."

Q: In the United Sates, there once was a state of Franklin. Where was it located?

Q: Did the Japanese invade the United States during the Second World War?

A: Not for nothing was the latter half of the 19th century called the Victorian Age—Victoria was Queen of the United Kingdom of Great Britain and Ireland from 1837 until her death in 1901. Her husband was Prince Consort Albert, from Saxe-Colburg-Gotha, a German state.

A: Benjamin Franklin.

A: In August 1784, delegates from what is now eastern Tennessee gathered in Jonesborough to study the issue of seceding from North Carolina. By December, separation was a done deal. They named the new state Franklin, after Benjamin Franklin, one of America's founding fathers. Franklin's only governor was John Sevier. The state of Franklin disappeared forever when it was ceded to a new federal government in the late 1780s.

A: Yes, Alaska. In June 1942, Japanese troops invaded the Aleutian Islands of Agattu, Attu, and Kiska. American forces drove the Japanese out in 1943.

Q: Each of the following familiar quotes is taken from a play by William Shakespeare. From which play is each taken?
"The lady doth protest too much, methinks."
"To be or not to be: that is the question."
"Something is rotten in the state of Denmark."
"To sleep, perchance to dream."
"I must be cruel only to be kind."
"The play's the thing Wherein I'll catch the conscience of the King."

Q: What famous American said "You can fool all the people some of the time, and some of the people all the time, but you cannot fool all the people all the time"?

Q: What famous American said, "Politics is not a bad profession. If you succeed there are many rewards, if you disgrace yourself you can always write a book"?

A: All of them are from *Hamlet*.

A: Sixteenth President of the United States, Abraham Lincoln.

A: Thirty-ninth President of the United States, Ronald Reagan.

Q: What did President Harry S. Truman say about getting things done?

Q: What is Gracie Allen's mother's solution for preparing dinner for eight people?

Q: What do we call the days in which the Sun's path is farthest from the equator?

Q: How many medals did Jim Thorpe win at the 1912 Stockholm Olympic games?

Q: What actor played Jim Thorpe in the 1951 movie, *Jim Thorpe—All American*?

A: "It is amazing what you can accomplish if you do not care who gets the credit. "

A: According to Gracie Allen, "When my mother had to get dinner for eight, she'd just make enough for sixteen, and only serve half."

A: The summer and winter solstices, which fall on June 21 or 22 and December 21 or 22 of each year. The solstices are either of the two moments in the year when the Sun's path is farthest north or south from the equator. In the Northern Hemisphere, the summer solstice is the longest day of the year, measured by the amount of daylight, and the winter solstice is the shortest day.

A: In 1912, Native American James "Jim" Thorpe won the decathlon and the pentathlon by wide margins at the Olympic Games in Stockholm. But, the Amateur Athletic Union stripped him of his gold medals after they discovered that he had been paid to play semiprofessional baseball in 1909. Years after Thorpe's death in 1953, his amateur status was restored, and his Olympic gold medals were given to his family in 1983.

A: Burt Lancaster.

Q: Who invented the assembly line?

Q: Who invented the radio?

Q: Who invented vulcanized rubber?

Q: Who invented the lighter-than-air vehicle named the zeppelin?

A: Automobile manufacturer Ransom E. Olds introduced the moving assembly line in 1901. Henry Ford, who is often credited with inventing the assembly line, improved the assembly line by installing conveyer belts, which speeded up the process considerably.

A: Guglielmo Marconi (1874–1937) was an Italian physicist and inventor of a successful system of radiotelegraphy (1895). He later worked on the development of short-wave wireless communication, which constitutes the basis of nearly all modern long-distance radio. Marconi shared the Nobel Prize in physics in 1909.

A: Charles Goodyear discovered that, by mixing the crude rubber with sulfur and heating the mixture for a long time, rubber was transformed into the elastic material we know today. He named the process vulcanizing.

A: Count Ferdinand Graf von Zeppelin (1838–1917) was the German military officer who developed the rigid dirigible that became known as the zeppelin. The airship's first trial was in July 1900. Although zeppelins had some popularity, and passengers made many trips without accidents or loss of life, they are perhaps best remembered because of the tragic explosion of the *Hindenburg* on May 6, 1937, in Lakehurst, New Jersey. Thirty-six people died.

Q: Who invented the windshield wiper?

Q: Who was the first scientist to discover the many uses of peanuts, including peanut butter?

Q: Who invented the safety pin?

Q: Who invented the motorcycle?

A: Mary Anderson was granted her first patent for a window-cleaning device in November 1903. Her invention could clean snow, rain, or sleet from a windshield by using a handle inside the car. Windshield wipers were standard equipment on all American cars by 1916.

A: Born a slave in Mississippi, George Washington Carver (1864–1943) developed several hundred uses for peanuts, sweet potatoes, and soybeans, and developed a new type of cotton known as Carver's hybrid. Carver dedicated his life to bettering the position of African-Americans and improving the economic prospects of the South.

A: The safety pin was invented by Walter Hunt of New York while he was absent-mindedly twisting a piece of wire. On April 10, 1849, Hunt patented the safety pin, but he later sold the patent for a few hundred dollars. His invention made babies very grateful.

A: In 1867, Sylvester Howard Roper of Roxbury, Massachusetts built a steam-powered motorcycle. But, German inventor Gottlieb Daimler is credited with building the first modern motorcycle in 1885, which was powered by a single-cylinder gas-powered engine. Daimler later teamed up with Karl Benz, forming the Daimler-Benz Corporation, to make automobiles.

Q: What French aristocrat helped the American colonists out during the American Revolution?

Q: What French pirate helped out the Americans during the War of 1812?

Q: Who played Jean Lafitte in the 1958 film, *The Buccaneer*?

Q: Which scientist was the first to suggest that the earth traveled around the Sun, rather than the other way around?

A: Marquis de Lafayette (1757–1834) was a French aristocrat who offered his services, and fought with the American colonists against the British in the American Revolution. Given a commission as a major general by the colonists, Lafayette fought with distinction, particularly at the Battle of Brandywine, Pennsylvania, in 1777. After the war, he returned to France; on visits to the new United States of America, he was treated like a hero.

A: Jean Lafitte, a privateer and smuggler, interrupted his pirating activities to join the fight for the United States against the British at the Battle of New Orleans (December 1814–January 1815). For his help, Andrew Jackson personally commended Laffite, and President James Madison issued a pardon for Lafitte and his men.

A: Dark-haired Yul Brynner was Jean Lafitte in the 1958 remake of a 1938 film. Frederic March played Lafitte in the 1938 film.

A: Nicolaus Copernicus (1473–1543) was a Polish astronomer who proposed that the Earth is a planet that orbits the Sun annually. This representation of the heavens is called the heliocentric, or "Sun-centered" view of the planets.

Q: Who invented basketball?

Q: When was volleyball invented?

Q: Rank these international cities by amount of average annual rainfall: San Francisco, New York, London, Dublin.

Q: What states are the five most populous?

Q: Which five states have the lowest populations?

A: In 1891, trying to create an indoor athletic activity for male students at the School for Christian Workers in Springfield, Massachusetts, James Naismith developed basketball and its original thirteen rules.

A: Not far from Springfield, in the city of Holyoke, Massachusetts, in 1895, William Morgan, a YMCA instructor, created the game of volleyball, which he called *mintonette.* Morgan borrowed elements from both tennis and handball. In 1900, a special ball was designed for the sport.

A: New York has by far the most rain. Average annual precipitation, ranked by wettest to driest: New York—46.7 inches, London—29.7 inches, Dublin—29.2 inches, San Francisco—20.4 inches.

A: California (33,871,648 population), Texas (20,851,820), New York (18,976,457), Florida (15,082,378), and Illinois (12,419,293) are the five states with the highest populations, as of the 2000 census. Pennsylvania is a close sixth, with 12,281,054 people.

A: As of April 1, 2000, Wyoming (493,782 population) has the fewest people of the fifty states of the United States. Vermont (608,827), Alaska (626,932), North Dakota (642,200), and South Dakota (754,844) round out the bottom five in population of the fifty United States.

Q: What does the state name *Oklahoma* mean in the Choctaw language?

Q: In what year was the "Great Blackout," when the whole Northeast of the United States was without electricity?

Q: Why are London police officers called "bobbies"?

Q: Nicknamed after Babe Ruth, what other great American athlete was called "Babe"?

A: The name "Oklahoma" comes from the Choctaw words: "okla" meaning people and "humma" meaning red, so the state's name literally means "red people."

A: On November 9, 1965, the whole northeastern United States, from Michigan to New England, as well as parts of Canada, New Jersey and Pennsylvania, was blacked out for up to thirteen hours, due to the failure of the power grid. The power outage—known as the "Great Blackout of 1965"—affected thirty million people—in New York City, people were caught in elevators and subway trains for hours and hours.

A: When Sir Robert Peel introduced his Act for Policing the Metropolis in 1829, the members of the Metropolitan Police (London's first police force) were nicknamed Bobbies after Sir Robert.

A: Mildred "Babe" Didrikson Zaharaias from Port Arthur, Texas. She excelled in many sports, including track and field, where she won several medals; and golf, where she won every major women's golf championship, including the U.S. amateur championship (1946), the world championship (1948, 1949, 1950, 1951), and the U.S. Women's Open (1948, 1950, and 1954).

Q: Who was Englebert Humperdink?

Q: When did Coca-Cola® introduce "New Coke"?

Q: What was the name of the Ramones's first album? What were the first names of the members of the band?

Q: Why should you be concerned if your elderly grandparent suddenly likes rock and roll?

Q: Does your body temperature stay the same throughout the day?

A: Humperdink (1854–1921) was a German composer, whose best-known opera is *Hansel & Gretel*. Englebert Humperdink is also the name that Arnold Dorsey adopted in his pop music career, singing such songs as "Please Release Me."

A: In 1985, Coca-Cola® decided to change the ninety-nine year formula of Coke, and introduced "New Coke." After the public outcry, they brought back a version of the original formula.

A: Their 1976 debut album was called *The Ramones*. All of the Ramones took the surname Ramone; at the time of their first record, the first names of the band were Joey, Johnny, Dee Dee, and Tommy. Many consider the Ramones to be the world's first punk band.

A: According to a recent report by researchers at Italy's National Center for Research and Care of Alzheimer's Disease, sudden changes in musical taste may be an indication that an elderly person is suffering from dementia.

A: Typically, a person's body temperature rises during the late afternoon and drops late at night.

Q: When did Americans start drinking tea?

Q: When was the submarine first used in combat?

Q: Where were Tonka® trucks first manufactured?

Q: Why does the Tower of Pisa lean?

A: Governor Peter Stuyvesant brought the first tea to the Dutch settlement of New Amsterdam around 1650. Settlers there quickly adopted the new beverage. In fact, when the English arrived, they found that the small settlement, which they re-named New York, consumed more tea at that time then all of England.

A: In 1776, American David Bushnell built a human-powered, one-man submarine named the *Turtle*. It was able to dive and surface, and he made three unsuccessful attempts to sink British warships and break the British blockade of New York harbor during the Revolutionary War.

A: Tonka Toy trucks were first designed and manufactured in 1947 by the Mound Metalcraft Company, a small garden tool manufacturer located in a schoolhouse basement near Lake Minnetonka, Minnesota. The first two toys were a steam shovel and a crane.

A: Pisa's Leaning Tower was originally built (1173-1350) on soft, sandy soil, with a shallow foundation. Over the centuries, various efforts have been made to reduce the tilt—the latest includes adding weights, and the careful removal of soil under one side of the base. Of course, it will not be made to stand straight—it's too much of a tourist attraction.

Q: When was the Coronation of Great Britain's Queen Elizabeth II?

Q: How many of the twenty highest peaks in the world are in North America?

Q: How many of the United States's twenty highest mountains are in the 48 contiguous states?

Q: What was the first U.S. National Park?

Q: Which national park has the most visitors?

Q: What elements are the main components of air on earth?

Q: How much of the earth's surface is covered with ice?

A: Elizabeth the Second, Queen of the United Kingdom of Great Britain and Northern Ireland and Her other Realms and Territories, Head of the Commonwealth, Defender of the Faith, was crowned on June 2, 1953 at London's Westminster Abbey. However, she had ascended to the British throne several months previously, on February 6, 1952, after the death of her father, King George VI.

A: None. All of the twenty highest peaks in the world are in the Himalayas, in Asia.

A: Only one—Mt. Whitney, in California, is the seventeenth highest peak in the United States, at 14,494 feet. The other nineteen highest peaks are in Alaska.

A: Yosemite National Park, which opened on March 1, 1872.

A: With approximately ten million visitors a year, the Great Smoky Mountains National Park, on the Tennessee-North Carolina border, drew nearly twice the number of visitors as the second most-visited park, the Grand Canyon.

A: Air is primarily composed of nitrogen and oxygen.

A: About ten per cent of the earth's surface is covered with ice. The icy cover has ranged from about 10 percent to around 30 percent during the last Ice Age.